the source

arrangements for worship groups

book 6

B♭ instruments

arranged by Chris Mitchell

Kevin Mayhew

We hope you enjoy the music in this book.
Further copies of this and the other books in the series are available
from your local music shop or Christian bookshop.

In case of difficulty, please contact the publisher direct:

The Sales Department
KEVIN MAYHEW LTD
Rattlesden
Bury St Edmunds
Suffolk IP30 0SZ

Phone 01449 737978
Fax 01449 737834
E-mail info@kevinmayhewltd.com

Please ask for our complete catalogue of outstanding Church Music.

First published in Great Britain in 1998 by Kevin Mayhew Ltd.

© Copyright 1998 Kevin Mayhew Ltd.

ISBN 1 84003 133 6
ISMN M 57004 216 6
Catalogue No: 1470312
0 1 2 3 4 5 6 7 8 9

Cover designed by Jaquetta Sergeant

Music arrangements by Chris Mitchell

Music setting by Chris Mitchell and Lynwen Davies

Printed and bound in Great Britain

Contents

This index gives the first line of each hymn. If a hymn is known by an alternative title, this is also given, but indented and in italics.

CHRIS MITCHELL is a well-established arranger, composer, musical director and session musician who has worked with Graham Kendrick, David Peacock, Gloria Gaynor and the BBC. He and his wife, Linda, are experienced worship leaders and are involved in providing seminars and workshops for Christians in the arts.

501 There's a wind a-blowing

(Sweet wind)
David Ruis

3 verses

502 There's no one like you

Eddie Espinosa

2 verses

503 These are the days
(Days of Elijah)

Robin Mark

2 verses

504 The Spirit of the sovereign Lord

Andy Park

2 verses

505 The steadfast love of the Lord

Edith McNeil

506 The trumpets sound, the angels sing
(The feast is ready)

Graham Kendrick

3 verses

507 The Word made flesh
(We await a Saviour from heaven)

Wes Sutton

3 verses

508 The world is looking for a hero
(Champion)

Noel and Tricia Richards

2 verses

509 They that wait

Kevin Prosch

510 Thine be the glory

George Frideric Handel

3 verses

511 This Child

Graham Kendrick

3 verses

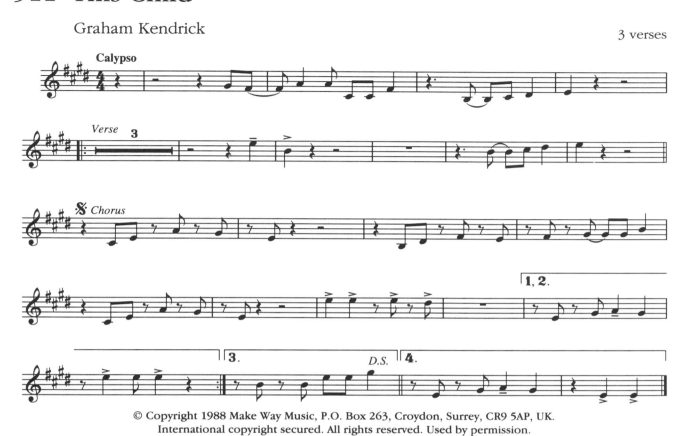

512 This grace is mine
(The power and the glory)

Geoff Bullock

3 verses

513 This, in essence, is the message
(God is light)

Gary Sadler and Lynn DeShazo

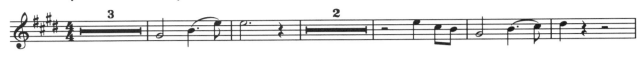

514 This is my beloved Son
(That the Lamb who was slain)

Graham Kendrick   3 verses

515 This is my desire
(I give you my heart)

Reuben Morgan

516 This is the day that the Lord has made

Bob Fitts

517 This is the day

Les Garrett

Brightly, with pace

518 This is the message of the cross
(Message of the cross)

Martin Smith

3 verses

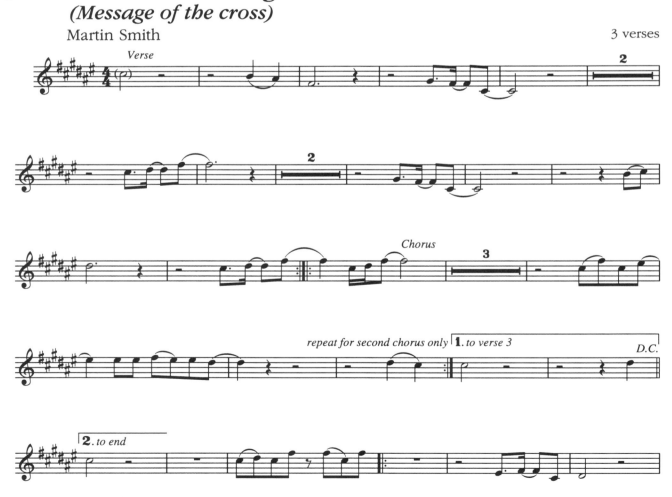

519 This is the mystery
(Let the Bride say, 'Come')

Philip Lawson Johnston and Chris Bowater

3 verses

520 This is the sweetest mystery

Andy Piercy and Dave Clifton

2 verses

521 This love
(Now is the time)

Geoff Bullock

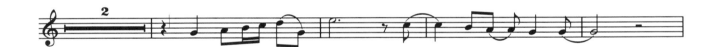

522 Though I feel afraid
(All I know)

Ian White

2 verses

523 Though the earth should tremble
(I worship you, eternal God)

Mark Altrogge

2 verses

524 To be in your presence
(My desire)

Noel Richards

2 verses

With intimacy

525 To every good thing God is doing
(Amen)

Bob Fitts

526 To God be the glory!

William Howard Doane

3 verses

527 To keep your lovely face

Graham Kendrick

528 Tonight
(Glory to God)

Graham Kendrick

2 verses

529 To you, O Lord, I bring my worship
(Release my soul)

Craig Musseau

530 To you, O Lord, I lift my soul

Graham Kendrick

2 verses

Verse 3

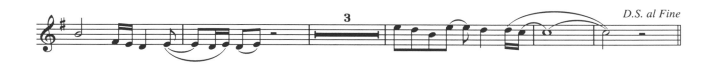

531 Turn our hearts

Graham Kendrick

4 verses

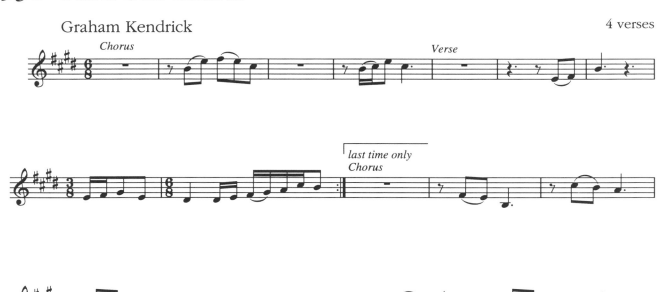

532 Turn to me and be saved

Graham Kendrick

533 Turn your eyes upon Jesus

Helen H. Lemmel

534 Wake up, my soul

Matt Redman

2 verses

535 Wake up, O sleeper

Graham Kendrick

3 verses

536 We are a people of power

Trevor King

Driving Rock

537 We are his children
(Go forth in his name)

Graham Kendrick

3 verses

With life

538 We are his people
(Shout to the Lord)

Kevin Prosch

2 verses

In a steady half-time

539 We are marching

3 verses

Traditional African

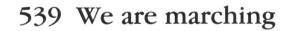

540 We are the army of God
(Army of God)

Kevin Prosch

With a steady rhythm

541 We believe

Graham Kendrick

2 verses

With strength

542 We bring the sacrifice of praise

Kirk Dearman

543 We come into your presence
(Father of creation)

Robert Eastwood

544 We declare your majesty

Malcolm du Plessis

545 We do not presume
(Prayer of humble access)

Andy Piercy

546 We have a great priest

2 verses

Dave Clifton

547 We have prayed that you would have mercy
(Let it rain)

Paul Oakley

548 Welcome, King of kings

Noel Richards

2 verses

Brightly, with strength

Chorus

549 Welcome the King

Graham Kendrick

2 verses

550 Well, I hear they're singing in the streets
(I've found Jesus)

Martin Smith

2 verses

551 We'll walk the land
(Let the flame burn brighter)

Graham Kendrick

3 verses

552 We march to the tune of a love-song
(We lift up a shout)

Steven Fry

2 verses

553 We must work together
(We'll see it all)

Ian Mizen and Andy Pressdee

554 We rejoice in the goodness of our God

Carol Owen

2 verses

555 We serve a God of miracles
(We serve a God of power)

Mark Altrogge

2 verses

556 We shall stand

Graham Kendrick

2 verses

557 We've had a light
(Surely the time has come)

Matt Redman

558 We want to remain in your love

Andy Piercy and Dave Clifton

559 We want to see Jesus lifted high

Doug Horley

560 We will cross every border
(Cross every border)

Graham Kendrick

4 verses

Fairly slow, with strength

561 We will run and not grow weary
(We will wait)

Tricia Allen and Martin J. Nystrom

562 We will turn the hearts

Kath Hall

Calypso feel

563 We will worship the Lamb of glory

Dennis Jernigan

2 verses

564 We worship and adore you

Andy Piercy

3 verses

565 What a friend I've found
(Jesus, friend for ever)

2 verses

Martin Smith

566 What a friend we have in Jesus

Charles Crozat Converse

3 verses

567 What kind of greatness

Graham Kendrick

3 verses

568 What kind of love is this

Bryn and Sally Haworth

3 verses

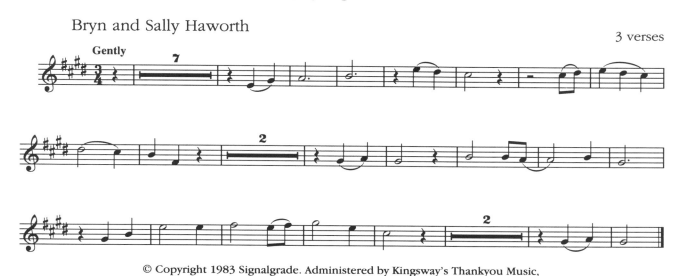

569 What noise shall we make

Lucy East

6 verses

570 When I feel the touch

Keri Jones and David Matthew

571 When I look into your holiness

Wayne and Cathy Perrin

572 When I survey the wondrous cross

Music adapted by Edward Miller

4 verses

572a When I survey the wondrous cross

Somerset folk song collected by Cecil Sharp

4 verses

573 When my heart is overwhelmed
(Lead me to the rock)

Lynn DeShazo

2 verses

574 When peace like a river

Philip Bliss

4 verses

575 When the Lord brought us back
(Psalm 126)

Graham Kendrick

576 When the music fades
(The heart of worship)

Matt Redman

2 verses

577 Where there once was only hurt
(Mourning into dancing)

Tommy Walker

578 Where two or three

Graham Kendrick

579 Who can sound the depths of sorrow

Graham Kendrick

5 verses

580 Who sees it all

Graham Kendrick

5 verses

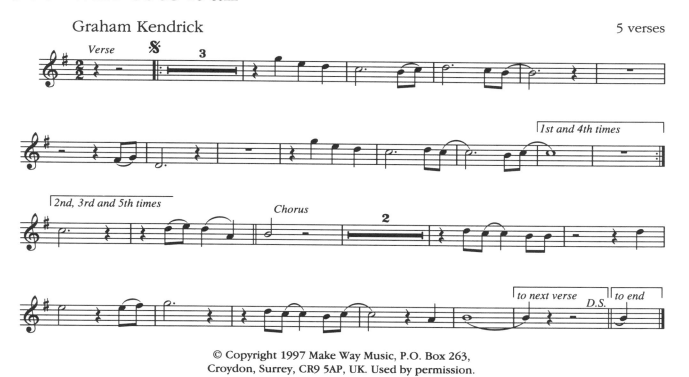

581 With all my heart

Steve McGregor

2 verses

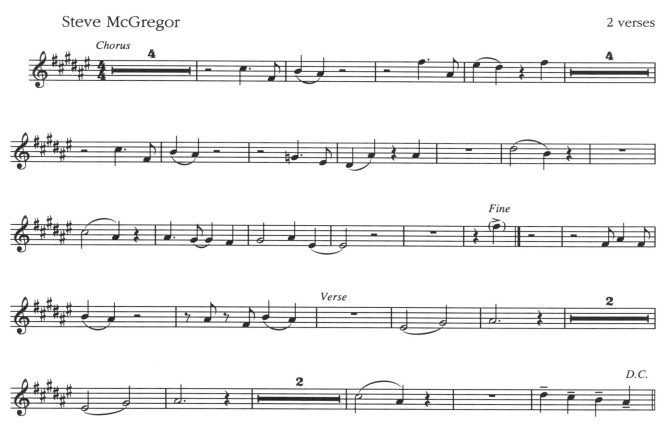

582 With my whole heart

Graham Kendrick

3 verses

Joyfully, with a swing

583 With this bread

Geoff Baker

2 verses

584 Worthy is the Lamb

Eddie Espinosa

585 Worthy, O worthy are you, Lord

Mark S. Kinzer

586 Yahweh

Andy Park

2 verses

587 Yet this will I call to mind
(Because of the Lord's great love)

Carl Tuttle

2 verses

588 You alone, Lord, are wonderful

Carol Owen

Chorus

589 You are beautiful
(I stand in awe)

Mark Altrogge

590 You are crowned with many crowns

John Sellers

591 You are God, you are great

Carol Owen

2 verses

592 You are Lord

Trish Morgan

593 You are merciful to me

Ian White

594 You are mighty

Craig Musseau

595 You are my King

Brian Doerksen

596 You are my passion

Noel and Tricia Richards

597 You are my rock

Jarrod Cooper and Sharon Pearce

2 verses

598 You have called us

Lynn DeShazo and Martin J. Nystrom

2 verses

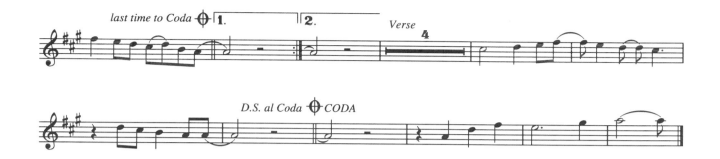

599 You have shown me
(I give thanks)
Brian Thiessen

2 verses

600 You have taken the precious
(So come)
Kevin Prosch and Tom Davis

601 You laid aside your majesty
(I really want to worship you, my Lord)
Noel Richards

602 You love me as you found me
(Your love keeps following me)

Russell Fragar

2 verses

603 You make my heart feel glad

Patricia Morgan and Sue Rinaldi

2 verses

604 You make your face to shine on me
(And that my soul knows very well)

Darlene Zschech and Russell Fragar

2 verses

605 You rescued me

Geoff Bullock

606 You're the Lion of Judah
(Lion of Judah)
Robin Mark

2 verses

607 Your love flows like a river

Scott Brenner and Michele Brenner

2 verses

608 Your mercy flows

Wes Sutton

Majestically

Verse

3 verses

609 You shall go out with joy
(The trees of the field)

Steffi Geiser Rubin and Stuart Dauermann

Lightly

610 This is the time
(Distant thunder)
David Palmer